Table of Content

Ways to Use This Plan Book 2

Seating Chart 3

Student Roster 4

Substitute Teacher Information 6

Year at a Glance 8

Components of the Lesson Plan Guide 9

Resources for the Teacher . . . .
- Objective Writer 11
- Assessment Generator 12
- Assessment Planning Guide Based on Bloom's Taxonomy 13
- Assessment Guide Incorporating Bloom's Taxonomy/Learning Standards 14
- Professional Development Plan Outline . 15

Daily Lesson Plan Pages 16–95

Notes 96

This lesson plan book belongs to:

Name ______________________________

School ______________________________

Grade/Subject ______________________________

Room ______________________________

School Year ______________________________

Address ______________________________

Phone ______________________________

Author: Lori R. Gehrke, M.Ed.

Teacher Created Resources, Inc.
6421 Industry Way
Westminster, CA 92683
www.teachercreated.com

ISBN: 978-0-7439-3627-9

Reprinted, 2007

Made in U.S.A.

Editor: Walter Kelly, M.A.

Managing Editor: Ina Massler Levin, M.A.

Cover Art: Wendy Roy

Imaging: Ralph Olmedo, Jr.,
Rosa C. See

Ways to Use This Plan Book

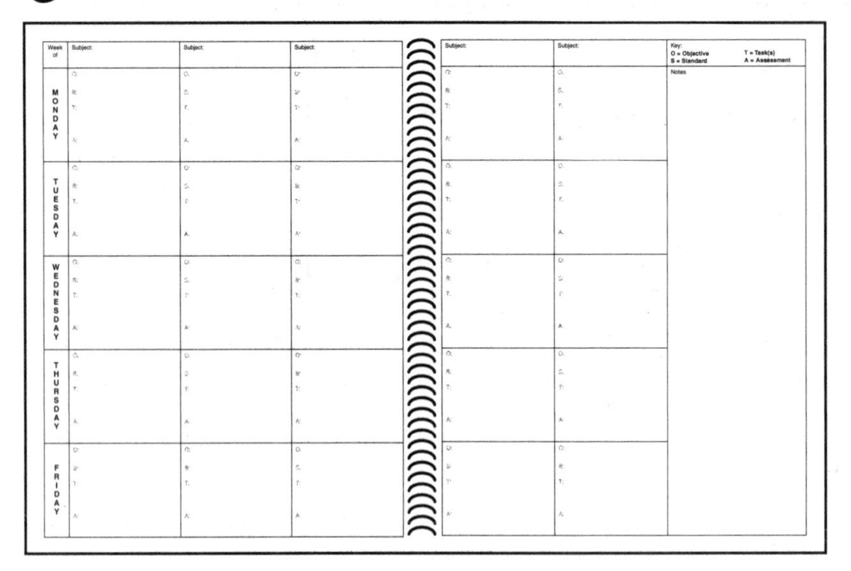

Purpose

Effective lesson planning is at the heart of student learning. How can weekly and daily lesson plans be aligned with state standards? How can the process of lesson planning and instruction help students meet the standards? This is an important part of the continuing challenge of higher standards for all students and accountability for learning.

Teachers using this lesson-planning guide will be provided the opportunity to outline their interdisciplinary units of study. This guide provides teachers resources they need to plan lessons that incorporate all areas of the curriculum, meet district and state standards, and link curriculum and instruction to assessment. This guide will serve not only as an interdisciplinary planning guide but also will assist teachers in meeting state performance standards; it can also be used as a tool for teacher professional development and incorporated into the current evaluation process.

How to Use the Guide

Use this guide to plan a week in advance rather than a day-to-day plan. Teachers may record the objectives covered in each subject throughout the week. They may align student and teacher performance tasks to the state performance standards. Once teachers have listed the objectives, they may record the resources and strategies that will be used to implement the objectives. As a final procedure the teacher can match district objectives and state standards. The teacher can record the assessment used to meet the objectives for the week. Copies of district curriculum and state standards can be stapled to the lesson guide and used to align the curriculum and assessments to these standards.

This guide should be used to help teachers monitor their instruction, record strategies used to meet objectives, link curriculum to assessment, and record state standards that are being addressed throughout the week.

Seating Chart (page 3)

Table or desk arrangement will vary depending on room size, grade level, and actual teaching style preferred. Suggestions have been given, but you may wish to customize your seating for your students.

Student Roster (pages 4 and 5)

Record both student and parent names and addresses. Make a special note of differences in last names when appropriate. You may wish to list siblings and their grades if they also attend your school. Notes may include special-needs children and medications necessary.

Substitute Teacher Information (pages 6 and 7)

Record all pertinent information on these pages. If you have a copy of the layout of your school, attach it to this page; otherwise, sketch an outline of the school grounds, showing restrooms, office, lounge, playground, etc. Paper-clip this page as well as the lesson plan page for easy reference.

Year at a Glance (page 8)

This section will give you an overview of the year and help focus on immediate and upcoming events, conferences, meetings, seminars, and other important dates. Record each event as soon as you are notified.

Daily Lesson Plans (pages 16–95)

Use the daily lesson plan pages to help organize your lesson plans for the week. In the blank that says "Week of ___________" add the dates for the week. You may wish to use the last column for notes, additions, or evaluation.

Seating Chart

Seat Arrangement Ideas

Sticky notes can be used to temporarily assign seats.

1. **Basic Row Seating**

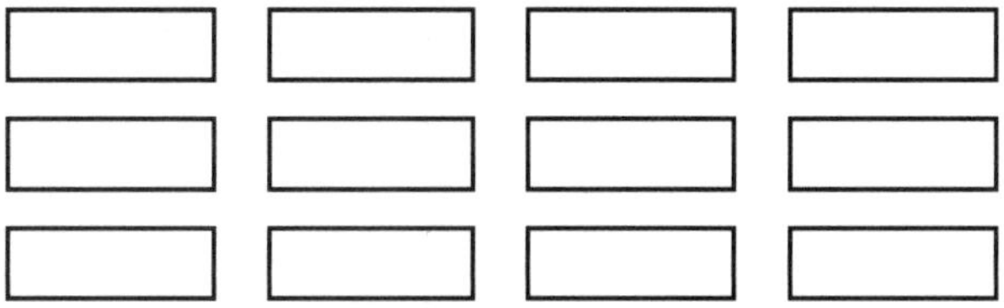

2. **U-Shaped Seating**

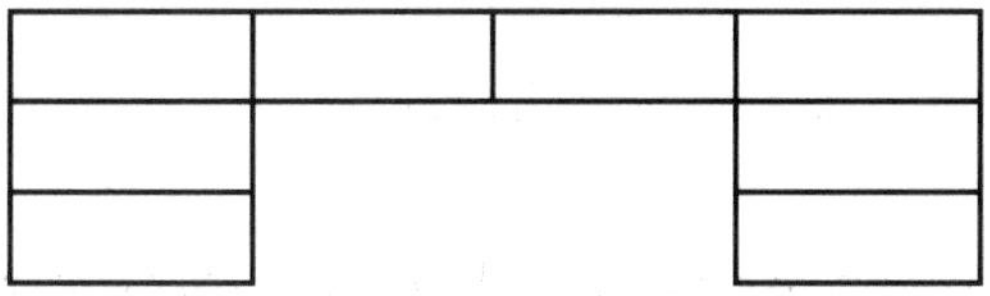

3. **Rectangle**

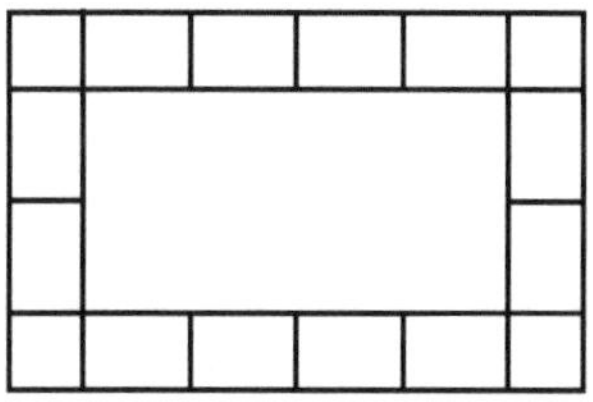

4. **Partner Seating**

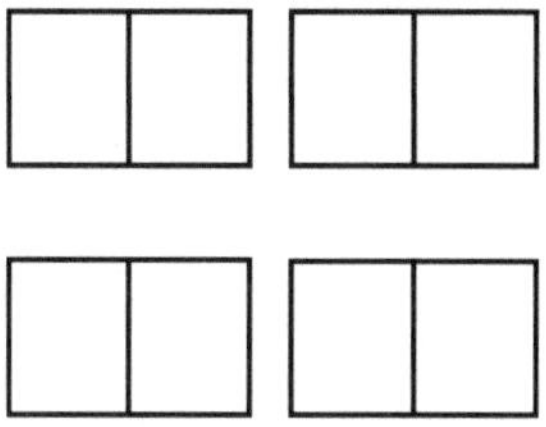

The size and shape of your room will play a large part in your seating arrangement.

You may want to change this layout once you are familiar with your students and their needs.

Regardless of your seating plan, the most important concern is that you can easily see all your students and the children in turn have good visibility of you, the chalkboard, and other focal points in the room.

Front of Classroom

Student Roster

Student's Name	Parents' Names	Address
1.		
2.		
3.		
4.		
5.		
6.		
7.		
8.		
9.		
10.		
11.		
12.		
13.		
14.		
15.		
16.		
17.		
18.		
19.		
20.		
21.		
22.		
23.		
24.		
25.		

Student Roster *(cont.)*

Home & Work Phones	Birthday	Siblings	Notes

Substitute Teacher Information

School Schedule

- Class Begins ____________
- Morning Recess ____________
- Lunchtime ____________
- Class Resumes ____________
- Afternoon Recess ____________
- Dismissal ____________

Special Notes

____

____

____

____

____

____

____

____

Special Classes

Student ____________

Class ________ Day ________ Time ________

Student ____________

Class ________ Day ________ Time ________

Student ____________

Class ________ Day ________ Time ________

Where to Find

- Class List ____________
- School Layout ____________
- Seating Chart ____________
- Attendance Record ____________
- Lesson Plans ____________
- Teacher Manuals ____________
- First Aid Kit ____________
- Emergency Information ____________
- Supplementary Activities ____________
- Class Supplies (paper, pencils, etc) ____________
- Referral Forms and Procedures ____________

____

____

____

____

____

____

____

____

____

____

____

____

Special Needs Students

Student	Needs	Time and Place

Substitute Teacher Information *(cont.)*

Classroom Standards

- When finished with an assignment
- When and how to speak out in class
- Incentive Program
- Discipline
- Restroom Procedure

People Who Can Help

- Teacher/Room
- Dependable Students
- Principal
- Secretary
- Custodian
- Counselor
- Nurse

Layout of School—including school office, teachers' lounge, restrooms, auditorium, playground, etc. (or attach printed diagram here)

Year at a Glance

August	September	October
November	December	January
February	March	April
May	June	July

Components of the Lesson Guide

The following directions explain how each section of the Lesson Planning Guide can be used to develop weekly or daily plans that align objectives, state standards, strategies, and performance tasks to assessments in all areas of the curriculum. The following sections are shown on the lesson plan key.

O = Objectives
Daily and weekly objectives are written to provide a focus for classroom instruction and student learning. These objectives could be generated using the various graphic organizers in this plan book or can correspond directly to district curriculum objectives.

S = Standards
This section provides a method of linking classroom objectives for the week with appropriate state standards across the curriculum. This documentation will allow continuous monitoring of the standards that are being incorporated into weekly and daily lessons. This documentation will also allow gaps and continued repetitions to be identified. Together, these procedures (linking and monitoring) will allow for modification of instruction to occur in order to meet district and state standards.

T = Tasks
These are direct activities that are performed by the teacher and the student throughout the week. The teacher tasks could involve modeling a strategy or any activity that relates directly to conducting the lesson. These tasks involve the direct instruction by the teacher in meeting the objectives for the week. The student tasks include those activities they will be engaged in throughout the week that will assist them in reaching the objectives for the week. Overall, this section can be thought of as direct activities conducted by both the teacher and the student throughout the week. Documentation of strategies used during the week in meeting the planned objectives and the resources used during the lessons may also be included in this section.

A = Assessments
Appropriate assessments can be incorporated into weekly and daily lesson plans. The various forms in this plan book can be used to plan assessments that are aligned to district objectives and state standards, as well as to Bloom's Taxonomy. This guide can be used to monitor the frequency that various forms of assessment are being used in the classroom.

Resources for the Teacher

Objective Writer

The objective writer is a tool that will assist in the development of daily objectives that are to be achieved in the classroom. The tool incorporates Bloom's Taxonomy indicators and appropriate products as a method of developing classroom objectives.

Assessment Generator

The assessment generator outlines classroom objectives, strategies, and skills with state standards. This tool will help to align classroom assessments with state and district curriculum.

Assessment Planning Guide Based on Bloom's Taxonomy

This assessment planning guide is basically a column chart of Bloom's six divisions: *knowledge, comprehension, application, analysis, synthesis,* and *evaluation.* The chart's columns are divided into an upper portion and a lower portion. The upper portion, labeled **Indicators**, contains a suggested listing of appropriate verbs to use in formulating your individual assessment guides for each unit plan. The lower portion, labeled **Assessment Forms**, contains a suggested listing of activities, projects, and assignments appropriate to measure or assess mastery in each of Bloom's six divisions.

Assessment Guide Incorporating Bloom's Taxonomy

The assessment guide is a graphic organizer that uses Bloom's Taxonomy in the development of classroom assessments. The guide organizes unit objectives, strategies that will be used to teach the objectives, state standards aligned to unit objectives, and the assessment/product that best matches each objective within the unit. Objectives that are developed for the unit can be designed according to Bloom's Taxonomy. This tool will allow differentiation of unit objectives to meet the needs of all students in the classroom.

Professional Development Plan Outline

The professional development plan provides a method for planning and implementing individual professional development. The outline provides a structure for developing goals that will continue professional growth and align to school improvement guidelines.

Notes

Following the actual lesson planning pages at the conclusion of the book a single page appears for additional listing of things to do, deadlines, progress, and comments relating to the listings. Naturally, this page is open for adjustment according to the teacher's wishes.

Objective Writer

Use this objective writer to generate the objectives in which you will engage students throughout the week. Circle one word from each column—A, B, and C—across the rows. Combine the words from each section to generate the new objective. For example, to write a "Knowledge" objective, a student or teacher could select the word *describe* from column A, the word *event* from column B, and the word *article* from column C. These key words would be used to generate the following objective: The learner will describe the major events in the story while writing an article for the newspaper.

	A	B	C	
	Activity/Indicator	**Domain**	**Assessment Product**	**Objective**
Knowledge	define, describe, memorize, recognize, identify, state, select, name, remember	fact, detail, name, date, place, event, concept, issue, problem, theme	newspaper, film, play, article, magazine	The learner will . . .
Comprehension	illustrate, match, interpret, predict, generalize, compare, summarize, explain, define	fact, detail, name, date, place, event, concept, issue, problem, theme	graph, cartoon, model, skit, summary, outline, diagram	
Application	solve, show, classify, prepare, produce, sketch, choose	fact, detail, name, date, place, event, concept, issue, problem, theme	painting, drama, diagram, photograph, paper, illustration, map, list	
Analysis	analyze, survey, categorize, infer, classify, select, subdivide	fact, detail, name, date, place, event, concept, issue, problem, theme	questionnaire, report, survey, graph	
Evaluation	combine, plan, organize, role-play, hypothesize, design, compose, create	fact, detail, name, date, place, event, concept, issue, problem, theme	article, game, report, play, experiment, invention, song, book	
Synthesis	compare, critique, summarize, judge, support, evaluate, relate	fact, detail, name, date, place, event, concept, issue, problem, theme	conclusion, self-evaluation, recommendation, group discussion, survey, debate, court trial	

Assessment Generator

This tool serves as a guide when planning the assessment prior to beginning a new unit of study. Use this tool to record the skills that will be assessed at the end of the unit, strategies used to teach the skills, and the state standards' connection to each skill.

	Skills Assessed	Strategies Used	State Standard
1.			
2.			
3.			
4.			
5.			

Assessment Planning Guide Based on Bloom's Taxonomy

	Knowledge	Comprehension		Application	Analysis	Synthesis	Evaluation
Indicators	define describe memorize recognize name identify state label locate recite select	convert rewrite change transform give examples illustrate paraphrase express restate match	compare extend interpret define predict distinguish generalize summarize explain relate infer	solve apply change choose use show sketch modify dramatize classify discover prepare produce paint	analyze classify survey distinguish categorize subdivide differentiate infer separate select point out	combine plan role-play invent compose revise design hypothesize construct create develop produce organize originate	compare appraise recommend critique judge criticize weigh support evaluate summarize relate consider
Assessment Forms	Events People Recordings Newspapers Magazine Articles Television Shows Text Readings Films A Play Filmstrip Radio	Graph Story Speech Own Statement Drama Photograph Tape Recording Cartoon Skit Diagram	Model Comparisons of Like or Unlike Items Summary Conclusion or Implication Based on Data Analogy Casual Relationships Outline	Diagram Sculpture Photograph Illustration Map List Drama Painting Solution Question Follow up Paper Smoothly Shift from one Gear to Another A Meeting	Questionnaire Parts of Propaganda Statement Identified A Syllogism Broken Down Report Survey A Conclusion Checked Graph	Article Game Experiment Invention Song Book Machine Report Set of Rules, Principles, or Standards Formulation of a Hypothesis or Question A Play Speculate on or Plan Alternative Courses of Action	Conclusion Self-Evaluation Recommendation Group Discussion Court Trial Survey Evaluation A Standard Compared Valuing

Assessment Guide Incorporating Bloom's Taxonomy/Learning Standards

Unit Planner

Bloom's Taxonomy	Objectives	Strategies	Standards	Assessment
Components	Students will be able to . . .	Teacher Tasks	State Standards	Which Matches the Need?
Knowledge				
Comprehension				
Application				
Analysis				
Synthesis				
Evaluation				

Professional Development Plan Outline

Participant: ______________________ **Grade:** ______________ **Content Area:** ______________

Start Date:

Professional Competencies:

Teaching Standards:

Professional Goals:

Professional Development Activities	Methods	Presenter	Time Frame	Resources/ Costs	Artifacts (Evidence)

Week of	Subject:	Subject:	Subject:
MONDAY	O: S: T: A:	O: S: T: A:	O: S: T: A:
TUESDAY	O: S: T: A:	O: S: T: A:	O: S: T: A:
WEDNESDAY	O: S: T: A:	O: S: T: A:	O: S: T: A:
THURSDAY	O: S: T: A:	O: S: T: A:	O: S: T: A:
FRIDAY	O: S: T: A:	O: S: T: A:	O: S: T: A:

Subject:	Subject:	Key: **O = Objective** **S = Standard** **T = Task(s)** **A = Assessment**
O: S: T: A:	O: S: T: A:	Notes
O: S: T: A:	O: S: T: A:	
O: S: T: A:	O: S: T: A:	
O: S: T: A:	O: S: T: A:	
O: S: T: A:	O: S: T: A:	

Week of	Subject:	Subject:	Subject:
MONDAY	O: S: T: A:	O: S: T: A:	O: S: T: A:
TUESDAY	O: S: T: A:	O: S: T: A:	O: S: T: A:
WEDNESDAY	O: S: T: A:	O: S: T: A:	O: S: T: A:
THURSDAY	O: S: T: A:	O: S: T: A:	O: S: T: A:
FRIDAY	O: S: T: A:	O: S: T: A:	O: S: T: A:

Subject:	Subject:	Key: **O = Objective** **T = Task(s)** **S = Standard** **A = Assessment**
O: S: T: A:	O: S: T: A:	Notes
O: S: T: A:	O: S: T: A:	
O: S: T: A:	O: S: T: A:	
O: S: T: A:	O: S: T: A:	
O: S: T: A:	O: S: T: A:	

Week of	Subject:	Subject:	Subject:
MONDAY	O: S: T: A:	O: S: T: A:	O: S: T: A:
TUESDAY	O: S: T: A:	O: S: T: A:	O: S: T: A:
WEDNESDAY	O: S: T: A:	O: S: T: A:	O: S: T: A:
THURSDAY	O: S: T: A:	O: S: T: A:	O: S: T: A:
FRIDAY	O: S: T: A:	O: S: T: A:	O: S: T: A:

Subject:	Subject:	Key: **O = Objective** **T = Task(s)** **S = Standard** **A = Assessment**
O: S: T: A:	O: S: T: A:	Notes
O: S: T: A:	O: S: T: A:	
O: S: T: A:	O: S: T: A:	
O: S: T: A:	O: S: T: A:	
O: S: T: A:	O: S: T: A:	

Week of	Subject:	Subject:	Subject:
MONDAY	O: S: T: A:	O: S: T: A:	O: S: T: A:
TUESDAY	O: S: T: A:	O: S: T: A:	O: S: T: A:
WEDNESDAY	O: S: T: A:	O: S: T: A:	O: S: T: A:
THURSDAY	O: S: T: A:	O: S: T: A:	O: S: T: A:
FRIDAY	O: S: T: A:	O: S: T: A:	O: S: T: A:

Subject:	Subject:	Key: **O = Objective** **T = Task(s)** **S = Standard** **A = Assessment**
O: S: T: A:	O: S: T: A:	Notes
O: S: T: A:	O: S: T: A:	
O: S: T: A:	O: S: T: A:	
O: S: T: A:	O: S: T: A:	
O: S: T: A:	O: S: T: A:	

Week of	Subject:	Subject:	Subject:
MONDAY	O: S: T: A:	O: S: T: A:	O: S: T: A:
TUESDAY	O: S: T: A:	O: S: T: A:	O: S: T: A:
WEDNESDAY	O: S: T: A:	O: S: T: A:	O: S: T: A:
THURSDAY	O: S: T: A:	O: S: T: A:	O: S: T: A:
FRIDAY	O: S: T: A:	O: S: T: A:	O: S: T: A:

Subject:	Subject:	Key: **O = Objective** **S = Standard** **T = Task(s)** **A = Assessment**
O: S: T: A:	O: S: T: A:	Notes
O: S: T: A:	O: S: T: A:	
O: S: T: A:	O: S: T: A:	
O: S: T: A:	O: S: T: A:	
O: S: T: A:	O: S: T: A:	

Week of	Subject:	Subject:	Subject:
MONDAY	O: S: T: A:	O: S: T: A:	O: S: T: A:
TUESDAY	O: S: T: A:	O: S: T: A:	O: S: T: A:
WEDNESDAY	O: S: T: A:	O: S: T: A:	O: S: T: A:
THURSDAY	O: S: T: A:	O: S: T: A:	O: S: T: A:
FRIDAY	O: S: T: A:	O: S: T: A:	O: S: T: A:

Subject:	Subject:	Key: **O = Objective** **T = Task(s)** **S = Standard** **A = Assessment**
O: S: T: A:	O: S: T: A:	Notes
O: S: T: A:	O: S: T: A:	
O: S: T: A:	O: S: T: A:	
O: S: T: A:	O: S: T: A:	
O: S: T: A:	O: S: T: A:	

Week of	Subject:	Subject:	Subject:
MONDAY	O: S: T: A:	O: S: T: A:	O: S: T: A:
TUESDAY	O: S: T: A:	O: S: T: A:	O: S: T: A:
WEDNESDAY	O: S: T: A:	O: S: T: A:	O: S: T: A:
THURSDAY	O: S: T: A:	O: S: T: A:	O: S: T: A:
FRIDAY	O: S: T: A:	O: S: T: A:	O: S: T: A:

Subject:	Subject:	Key: **O = Objective** **T = Task(s)** **S = Standard** **A = Assessment**
O: S: T: A:	O: S: T: A:	Notes
O: S: T: A:	O: S: T: A:	
O: S: T: A:	O: S: T: A:	
O: S: T: A:	O: S: T: A:	
O: S: T: A:	O: S: T: A:	

Week of	Subject:	Subject:	Subject:
MONDAY	O: S: T: A:	O: S: T: A:	O: S: T: A:
TUESDAY	O: S: T: A:	O: S: T: A:	O: S: T: A:
WEDNESDAY	O: S: T: A:	O: S: T: A:	O: S: T: A:
THURSDAY	O: S: T: A:	O: S: T: A:	O: S: T: A:
FRIDAY	O: S: T: A:	O: S: T: A:	O: S: T: A:

Subject:	Subject:	Key: **O = Objective** **T = Task(s)** **S = Standard** **A = Assessment**
O: S: T: A:	O: S: T: A:	Notes
O: S: T: A:	O: S: T: A:	
O: S: T: A:	O: S: T: A:	
O: S: T: A:	O: S: T: A:	
O: S: T: A:	O: S: T: A:	

Week of	Subject:	Subject:	Subject:
MONDAY	O: S: T: A:	O: S: T: A:	O: S: T: A:
TUESDAY	O: S: T: A:	O: S: T: A:	O: S: T: A:
WEDNESDAY	O: S: T: A:	O: S: T: A:	O: S: T: A:
THURSDAY	O: S: T: A:	O: S: T: A:	O: S: T: A:
FRIDAY	O: S: T: A:	O: S: T: A:	O: S: T: A:

Subject:	Subject:	Key: **O = Objective** **T = Task(s)** **S = Standard** **A = Assessment**
O: S: T: A:	O: S: T: A:	Notes
O: S: T: A:	O: S: T: A:	
O: S: T: A:	O: S: T: A:	
O: S: T: A:	O: S: T: A:	
O: S: T: A:	O: S: T: A:	

Week of	Subject:	Subject:	Subject:
MONDAY	O: S: T: A:	O: S: T: A:	O: S: T: A:
TUESDAY	O: S: T: A:	O: S: T: A:	O: S: T: A:
WEDNESDAY	O: S: T: A:	O: S: T: A:	O: S: T: A:
THURSDAY	O: S: T: A:	O: S: T: A:	O: S: T: A:
FRIDAY	O: S: T: A:	O: S: T: A:	O: S: T: A:

Subject:	Subject:	Key: **O = Objective** **S = Standard** **T = Task(s)** **A = Assessment**
O: S: T: A:	O: S: T: A:	Notes
O: S: T: A:	O: S: T: A:	
O: S: T: A:	O: S: T: A:	
O: S: T: A:	O: S: T: A:	
O: S: T: A:	O: S: T: A:	

Week of	Subject:	Subject:	Subject:
MONDAY	O: S: T: A:	O: S: T: A:	O: S: T: A:
TUESDAY	O: S: T: A:	O: S: T: A:	O: S: T: A:
WEDNESDAY	O: S: T: A:	O: S: T: A:	O: S: T: A:
THURSDAY	O: S: T: A:	O: S: T: A:	O: S: T: A:
FRIDAY	O: S: T: A:	O: S: T: A:	O: S: T: A:

Subject:	Subject:	Key: **O = Objective** **S = Standard** **T = Task(s)** **A = Assessment**
O: S: T: A:	O: S: T: A:	Notes
O: S: T: A:	O: S: T: A:	
O: S: T: A:	O: S: T: A:	
O: S: T: A:	O: S: T: A:	
O: S: T: A:	O: S: T: A:	

Week of	Subject:	Subject:	Subject:
MONDAY	O: S: T: A:	O: S: T: A:	O: S: T: A:
TUESDAY	O: S: T: A:	O: S: T: A:	O: S: T: A:
WEDNESDAY	O: S: T: A:	O: S: T: A:	O: S: T: A:
THURSDAY	O: S: T: A:	O: S: T: A:	O: S: T: A:
FRIDAY	O: S: T: A:	O: S: T: A:	O: S: T: A:

Subject:	Subject:	Key: **O = Objective** **T = Task(s)** **S = Standard** **A = Assessment**
O: S: T: A:	O: S: T: A:	Notes
O: S: T: A:	O: S: T: A:	
O: S: T: A:	O: S: T: A:	
O: S: T: A:	O: S: T: A:	
O: S: T: A:	O: S: T: A:	

Week of	Subject:	Subject:	Subject:
MONDAY	O: S: T: A:	O: S: T: A:	O: S: T: A:
TUESDAY	O: S: T: A:	O: S: T: A:	O: S: T: A:
WEDNESDAY	O: S: T: A:	O: S: T: A:	O: S: T: A:
THURSDAY	O: S: T: A:	O: S: T: A:	O: S: T: A:
FRIDAY	O: S: T: A:	O: S: T: A:	O: S: T: A:

Subject:	Subject:	Key: **O = Objective** **S = Standard** **T = Task(s)** **A = Assessment**
O: S: T: A:	O: S: T: A:	Notes
O: S: T: A:	O: S: T: A:	
O: S: T: A:	O: S: T: A:	
O: S: T: A:	O: S: T: A:	
O: S: T: A:	O: S: T: A:	

Week of	Subject:	Subject:	Subject:
MONDAY	O: S: T: A:	O: S: T: A:	O: S: T: A:
TUESDAY	O: S: T: A:	O: S: T: A:	O: S: T: A:
WEDNESDAY	O: S: T: A:	O: S: T: A:	O: S: T: A:
THURSDAY	O: S: T: A:	O: S: T: A:	O: S: T: A:
FRIDAY	O: S: T: A:	O: S: T: A:	O: S: T: A:

Subject:	Subject:	Key: **O = Objective** **T = Task(s)** **S = Standard** **A = Assessment**
O: S: T: A:	O: S: T: A:	Notes
O: S: T: A:	O: S: T: A:	
O: S: T: A:	O: S: T: A:	
O: S: T: A:	O: S: T: A:	
O: S: T: A:	O: S: T: A:	

Week of	Subject:	Subject:	Subject:
MONDAY	O: S: T: A:	O: S: T: A:	O: S: T: A:
TUESDAY	O: S: T: A:	O: S: T: A:	O: S: T: A:
WEDNESDAY	O: S: T: A:	O: S: T: A:	O: S: T: A:
THURSDAY	O: S: T: A:	O: S: T: A:	O: S: T: A:
FRIDAY	O: S: T: A:	O: S: T: A:	O: S: T: A:

Subject:	Subject:	Key: **O = Objective** **T = Task(s)** **S = Standard** **A = Assessment**
O: S: T: A:	O: S: T: A:	Notes
O: S: T: A:	O: S: T: A:	
O: S: T: A:	O: S: T: A:	
O: S: T: A:	O: S: T: A:	
O: S: T: A:	O: S: T: A:	

Week of	Subject:	Subject:	Subject:
MONDAY	O: S: T: A:	O: S: T: A:	O: S: T: A:
TUESDAY	O: S: T: A:	O: S: T: A:	O: S: T: A:
WEDNESDAY	O: S: T: A:	O: S: T: A:	O: S: T: A:
THURSDAY	O: S: T: A:	O: S: T: A:	O: S: T: A:
FRIDAY	O: S: T: A:	O: S: T: A:	O: S: T: A:

Subject:	Subject:	Key: **O = Objective** **S = Standard** **T = Task(s)** **A = Assessment**
O: S: T: A:	O: S: T: A:	Notes
O: S: T: A:	O: S: T: A:	
O: S: T: A:	O: S: T: A:	
O: S: T: A:	O: S: T: A:	
O: S: T: A:	O: S: T: A:	

Week of	Subject:	Subject:	Subject:
MONDAY	O: S: T: A:	O: S: T: A:	O: S: T: A:
TUESDAY	O: S: T: A:	O: S: T: A:	O: S: T: A:
WEDNESDAY	O: S: T: A:	O: S: T: A:	O: S: T: A:
THURSDAY	O: S: T: A:	O: S: T: A:	O: S: T: A:
FRIDAY	O: S: T: A:	O: S: T: A:	O: S: T: A:

Subject:	Subject:	Key: **O = Objective** **T = Task(s)** **S = Standard** **A = Assessment**
O: S: T: A:	O: S: T: A:	Notes
O: S: T: A:	O: S: T: A:	
O: S: T: A:	O: S: T: A:	
O: S: T: A:	O: S: T: A:	
O: S: T: A:	O: S: T: A:	

Week of	Subject:	Subject:	Subject:
MONDAY	O: S: T: A:	O: S: T: A:	O: S: T: A:
TUESDAY	O: S: T: A:	O: S: T: A:	O: S: T: A:
WEDNESDAY	O: S: T: A:	O: S: T: A:	O: S: T: A:
THURSDAY	O: S: T: A:	O: S: T: A:	O: S: T: A:
FRIDAY	O: S: T: A:	O: S: T: A:	O: S: T: A:

Subject:	Subject:	Key: **O = Objective** **T = Task(s)** **S = Standard** **A = Assessment**
O: S: T: A:	O: S: T: A:	Notes
O: S: T: A:	O: S: T: A:	
O: S: T: A:	O: S: T: A:	
O: S: T: A:	O: S: T: A:	
O: S: T: A:	O: S: T: A:	

Week of	Subject:	Subject:	Subject:
MONDAY	O: S: T: A:	O: S: T: A:	O: S: T: A:
TUESDAY	O: S: T: A:	O: S: T: A:	O: S: T: A:
WEDNESDAY	O: S: T: A:	O: S: T: A:	O: S: T: A:
THURSDAY	O: S: T: A:	O: S: T: A:	O: S: T: A:
FRIDAY	O: S: T: A:	O: S: T: A:	O: S: T: A:

Subject:	Subject:	Key: **O = Objective** **S = Standard** **T = Task(s)** **A = Assessment**
O: S: T: A:	O: S: T: A:	Notes
O: S: T: A:	O: S: T: A:	
O: S: T: A:	O: S: T: A:	
O: S: T: A:	O: S: T: A:	
O: S: T: A:	O: S: T: A:	

Week of	Subject:	Subject:	Subject:
MONDAY	O: S: T: A:	O: S: T: A:	O: S: T: A:
TUESDAY	O: S: T: A:	O: S: T: A:	O: S: T: A:
WEDNESDAY	O: S: T: A:	O: S: T: A:	O: S: T: A:
THURSDAY	O: S: T: A:	O: S: T: A:	O: S: T: A:
FRIDAY	O: S: T: A:	O: S: T: A:	O: S: T: A:

Subject:	Subject:	Key: **O = Objective** **T = Task(s)** **S = Standard** **A = Assessment**
O: S: T: A:	O: S: T: A:	Notes
O: S: T: A:	O: S: T: A:	
O: S: T: A:	O: S: T: A:	
O: S: T: A:	O: S: T: A:	
O: S: T: A:	O: S: T: A:	

Week of	Subject:	Subject:	Subject:
MONDAY	O: S: T: A:	O: S: T: A:	O: S: T: A:
TUESDAY	O: S: T: A:	O: S: T: A:	O: S: T: A:
WEDNESDAY	O: S: T: A:	O: S: T: A:	O: S: T: A:
THURSDAY	O: S: T: A:	O: S: T: A:	O: S: T: A:
FRIDAY	O: S: T: A:	O: S: T: A:	O: S: T: A:

<table>
<tr><td>Subject:</td><td>Subject:</td><td>Key:
O = Objective T = Task(s)
S = Standard A = Assessment</td></tr>
<tr><td>O:

S:

T:

A:</td><td>O:

S:

T:

A:</td><td rowspan="5">Notes</td></tr>
<tr><td>O:

S:

T:

A:</td><td>O:

S:

T:

A:</td></tr>
<tr><td>O:

S:

T:

A:</td><td>O:

S:

T:

A:</td></tr>
<tr><td>O:

S:

T:

A:</td><td>O:

S:

T:

A:</td></tr>
<tr><td>O:

S:

T:

A:</td><td>O:

S:

T:

A:</td></tr>
</table>

Week of	Subject:	Subject:	Subject:
MONDAY	O: S: T: A:	O: S: T: A:	O: S: T: A:
TUESDAY	O: S: T: A:	O: S: T: A:	O: S: T: A:
WEDNESDAY	O: S: T: A:	O: S: T: A:	O: S: T: A:
THURSDAY	O: S: T: A:	O: S: T: A:	O: S: T: A:
FRIDAY	O: S: T: A:	O: S: T: A:	O: S: T: A:

Subject:	Subject:	Key: **O = Objective** **T = Task(s)** **S = Standard** **A = Assessment**
O: S: T: A:	O: S: T: A:	Notes
O: S: T: A:	O: S: T: A:	
O: S: T: A:	O: S: T: A:	
O: S: T: A:	O: S: T: A:	
O: S: T: A:	O: S: T: A:	

Week of	Subject:	Subject:	Subject:
MONDAY	O: S: T: A:	O: S: T: A:	O: S: T: A:
TUESDAY	O: S: T: A:	O: S: T: A:	O: S: T: A:
WEDNESDAY	O: S: T: A:	O: S: T: A:	O: S: T: A:
THURSDAY	O: S: T: A:	O: S: T: A:	O: S: T: A:
FRIDAY	O: S: T: A:	O: S: T: A:	O: S: T: A:

Subject:	Subject:	Key: **O = Objective** **T = Task(s)** **S = Standard** **A = Assessment**
O: S: T: A:	O: S: T: A:	Notes
O: S: T: A:	O: S: T: A:	
O: S: T: A:	O: S: T: A:	
O: S: T: A:	O: S: T: A:	
O: S: T: A:	O: S: T: A:	

Week of	Subject:	Subject:	Subject:
MONDAY	O: S: T: A:	O: S: T: A:	O: S: T: A:
TUESDAY	O: S: T: A:	O: S: T: A:	O: S: T: A:
WEDNESDAY	O: S: T: A:	O: S: T: A:	O: S: T: A:
THURSDAY	O: S: T: A:	O: S: T: A:	O: S: T: A:
FRIDAY	O: S: T: A:	O: S: T: A:	O: S: T: A:

Subject:	Subject:	Key: **O = Objective** **T = Task(s)** **S = Standard** **A = Assessment**
O: S: T: A:	O: S: T: A:	Notes
O: S: T: A:	O: S: T: A:	
O: S: T: A:	O: S: T: A:	
O: S: T: A:	O: S: T: A:	
O: S: T: A:	O: S: T: A:	

Week of	Subject:	Subject:	Subject:
MONDAY	O: S: T: A:	O: S: T: A:	O: S: T: A:
TUESDAY	O: S: T: A:	O: S: T: A:	O: S: T: A:
WEDNESDAY	O: S: T: A:	O: S: T: A:	O: S: T: A:
THURSDAY	O: S: T: A:	O: S: T: A:	O: S: T: A:
FRIDAY	O: S: T: A:	O: S: T: A:	O: S: T: A:

Subject:	Subject:	Key: **O = Objective** **T = Task(s)** **S = Standard** **A = Assessment**
O: S: T: A:	O: S: T: A:	Notes
O: S: T: A:	O: S: T: A:	
O: S: T: A:	O: S: T: A:	
O: S: T: A:	O: S: T: A:	
O: S: T: A:	O: S: T: A:	

Week of	Subject:	Subject:	Subject:
MONDAY	O: S: T: A:	O: S: T: A:	O: S: T: A:
TUESDAY	O: S: T: A:	O: S: T: A:	O: S: T: A:
WEDNESDAY	O: S: T: A:	O: S: T: A:	O: S: T: A:
THURSDAY	O: S: T: A:	O: S: T: A:	O: S: T: A:
FRIDAY	O: S: T: A:	O: S: T: A:	O: S: T: A:

Subject:	Subject:	Key: **O = Objective** **T = Task(s)** **S = Standard** **A = Assessment**
O: S: T: A:	O: S: T: A:	Notes
O: S: T: A:	O: S: T: A:	
O: S: T: A:	O: S: T: A:	
O: S: T: A:	O: S: T: A:	
O: S: T: A:	O: S: T: A:	

Week of	Subject:	Subject:	Subject:
MONDAY	O: S: T: A:	O: S: T: A:	O: S: T: A:
TUESDAY	O: S: T: A:	O: S: T: A:	O: S: T: A:
WEDNESDAY	O: S: T: A:	O: S: T: A:	O: S: T: A:
THURSDAY	O: S: T: A:	O: S: T: A:	O: S: T: A:
FRIDAY	O: S: T: A:	O: S: T: A:	O: S: T: A:

Subject:	Subject:	Key: **O = Objective** **S = Standard** **T = Task(s)** **A = Assessment**
O: S: T: A:	O: S: T: A:	Notes
O: S: T: A:	O: S: T: A:	
O: S: T: A:	O: S: T: A:	
O: S: T: A:	O: S: T: A:	
O: S: T: A:	O: S: T: A:	

Week of	Subject:	Subject:	Subject:
MONDAY	O: S: T: A:	O: S: T: A:	O: S: T: A:
TUESDAY	O: S: T: A:	O: S: T: A:	O: S: T: A:
WEDNESDAY	O: S: T: A:	O: S: T: A:	O: S: T: A:
THURSDAY	O: S: T: A:	O: S: T: A:	O: S: T: A:
FRIDAY	O: S: T: A:	O: S: T: A:	O: S: T: A:

Subject:	Subject:	Key: **O = Objective** **S = Standard** **T = Task(s)** **A = Assessment**
O: S: T: A:	O: S: T: A:	Notes
O: S: T: A:	O: S: T: A:	
O: S: T: A:	O: S: T: A:	
O: S: T: A:	O: S: T: A:	
O: S: T: A:	O: S: T: A:	

Week of	Subject:	Subject:	Subject:
MONDAY	O: S: T: A:	O: S: T: A:	O: S: T: A:
TUESDAY	O: S: T: A:	O: S: T: A:	O: S: T: A:
WEDNESDAY	O: S: T: A:	O: S: T: A:	O: S: T: A:
THURSDAY	O: S: T: A:	O: S: T: A:	O: S: T: A:
FRIDAY	O: S: T: A:	O: S: T: A:	O: S: T: A:

Subject:	Subject:	Key: **O = Objective** **S = Standard** **T = Task(s)** **A = Assessment**
O: S: T: A:	O: S: T: A:	Notes
O: S: T: A:	O: S: T: A:	
O: S: T: A:	O: S: T: A:	
O: S: T: A:	O: S: T: A:	
O: S: T: A:	O: S: T: A:	

Week of	Subject:	Subject:	Subject:
MONDAY	O: S: T: A:	O: S: T: A:	O: S: T: A:
TUESDAY	O: S: T: A:	O: S: T: A:	O: S: T: A:
WEDNESDAY	O: S: T: A:	O: S: T: A:	O: S: T: A:
THURSDAY	O: S: T: A:	O: S: T: A:	O: S: T: A:
FRIDAY	O: S: T: A:	O: S: T: A:	O: S: T: A:

Subject:	Subject:	Key: **O = Objective** **T = Task(s)** **S = Standard** **A = Assessment**
O: S: T: A:	O: S: T: A:	Notes
O: S: T: A:	O: S: T: A:	
O: S: T: A:	O: S: T: A:	
O: S: T: A:	O: S: T: A:	
O: S: T: A:	O: S: T: A:	

Week of	Subject:	Subject:	Subject:
MONDAY	O: S: T: A:	O: S: T: A:	O: S: T: A:
TUESDAY	O: S: T: A:	O: S: T: A:	O: S: T: A:
WEDNESDAY	O: S: T: A:	O: S: T: A:	O: S: T: A:
THURSDAY	O: S: T: A:	O: S: T: A:	O: S: T: A:
FRIDAY	O: S: T: A:	O: S: T: A:	O: S: T: A:

Subject:	Subject:	Key: **O = Objective** **S = Standard** **T = Task(s)** **A = Assessment**
O: S: T: A:	O: S: T: A:	Notes
O: S: T: A:	O: S: T: A:	
O: S: T: A:	O: S: T: A:	
O: S: T: A:	O: S: T: A:	
O: S: T: A:	O: S: T: A:	

Week of	Subject:	Subject:	Subject:
MONDAY	O: S: T: A:	O: S: T: A:	O: S: T: A:
TUESDAY	O: S: T: A:	O: S: T: A:	O: S: T: A:
WEDNESDAY	O: S: T: A:	O: S: T: A:	O: S: T: A:
THURSDAY	O: S: T: A:	O: S: T: A:	O: S: T: A:
FRIDAY	O: S: T: A:	O: S: T: A:	O: S: T: A:

Subject:	Subject:	Key: **O = Objective** **T = Task(s)** **S = Standard** **A = Assessment**
O: S: T: A:	O: S: T: A:	Notes
O: S: T: A:	O: S: T: A:	
O: S: T: A:	O: S: T: A:	
O: S: T: A:	O: S: T: A:	
O: S: T: A:	O: S: T: A:	

Week of	Subject:	Subject:	Subject:
MONDAY	O: S: T: A:	O: S: T: A:	O: S: T: A:
TUESDAY	O: S: T: A:	O: S: T: A:	O: S: T: A:
WEDNESDAY	O: S: T: A:	O: S: T: A:	O: S: T: A:
THURSDAY	O: S: T: A:	O: S: T: A:	O: S: T: A:
FRIDAY	O: S: T: A:	O: S: T: A:	O: S: T: A:

Subject:	Subject:	Key: **O = Objective** **T = Task(s)** **S = Standard** **A = Assessment**
O: S: T: A:	O: S: T: A:	Notes
O: S: T: A:	O: S: T: A:	
O: S: T: A:	O: S: T: A:	
O: S: T: A:	O: S: T: A:	
O: S: T: A:	O: S: T: A:	

Notes

Things to Do	Deadline	Completed	In Progress	Comments